FOREWORD TO TEACHERS

IN compiling this course the objective has intentionally been not to cover too much ground; but rather to concentrate on the acquisition of a thorough musical background and a solid foundation in good clarinet playing. These two requisites are inseparable.

A brief section is devoted to the simpler rudiments of music which should be thoroughly understood as the need arises.

The learning of new fingerings as introduced should be insisted upon.

Cultivate in the pupil the habit of careful listening.

The familiar hymns and folk-songs have been selected because of their melodic interest as pieces, and because, in addition, in each appears some technical point to be mastered.

The value of learning to " think count" from the very beginning cannot be over-estimated. Only in this way can a pupil sense rhythm. Rhythm, one of the most essential elements of music, and usually conspicuous by its absence in amateur ensemble playing, is emphasized throughout.

Many teachers do the thinking for their pupils, instead of helping them to think for themselves. Insisting upon the mastery of each point will not dull their interest. What greater gratification can there be for a pupil, whether child or adult, than self-accomplishment in a set task?

Lessons marked, "Supplementary Material" may be given as a reward for well-prepared work.

Class teaching should be a combination of individual instruction and ensemble playing. At every lesson there should be individual playing so that all the necessary corrections can be made. Never allow pupils' mistakes to go unnoticed, since only by immediate correction will they develop the habit of careful thinking and playing.

A decided advantage of group-teaching is that it provides experience in ensemble playing and gives every pupil the opportunity of listening to the others, of observing their mistakes, and of profiting from the corrections.

For the best results each class should not be made up of more than six for a half-hour lesson, and twelve for an hour lesson. Irrespective of the numbers, the teacher must see to it that there is individual instruction as well as general class direction.

Classes should be regraded whenever necessary so as not to retard the progress of the more gifted students, or discourage the less musically endowed. This procedure also acts as an incentive for greater effort on the part of the pupils.

Lessons marked "Tongueing," "Scales and Arpeggios" and "Important Assignment" should be used whenever necessary according to the individual student's requirements.

The tests, following each five lessons, are given as a definite check on the pupil's progress of knowledge and accomplishment. These tests are most important and should not be omitted.

Eventual success in mastering the instrument depends on regular and careful application to its technical demands. Daily practice should not extend beyond the limits of the player's physical endurance—the aim should be the gradual development of lip and breath control alongside assured finger-work.

I wish to acknowledge my indebtedness to Mr. Otto Hansel, instructor of clarinet classes in the East Orange, N. J. Schools, for his helpful suggestions and criticisms in compiling this book.

C. PAUL HERFURTH
Director of Instrumental Music
East Orange, N. J.

RUDIMENTS OF MUSIC

Music is represented on paper by a combination of characters and signs, all of which it is necessary to learn in order to play the clarinet intelligently.

Symbols called notes are written upon and between five lines   ≡≡≡   which is the staff.

The sign 𝄞 placed at the beginning of the staff is called the treble or G clef.

The staff is divided by barlines into bars as follows:

Barline   Barline   Barline

Bar   Bar   Bar   Bar

These bars, in turn, are equal in time value, according to the fractional numbers, (Time signature) placed at the beginning of the music.

The time signature indicates the number of notes of equal value in each bar. The upper figure gives the number of beats or counts in a bar, and the lower figure indicates what kind of a note has one beat, such as $\frac{4}{4}$ or **C** equals

 four crotchets or the equivalent  minim and two crotchets in each bar ;

$\frac{2}{4}$ equals 2 crotchets; $\frac{4}{8}$ equals 4 quavers, etc.

There are different kinds of notes, each variety representing a certain time value as follows:

Semibreve equals: Two Minims, Four Crotchets, or Eight Quavers.

The count for the above would be, four to the semibreves; two to each minim; one to each crotchet and one to each group of two quavers.

The notes are named after the first seven letters of the alphabet, i.e., (a, b, c, d, e, f, g,) according to the line on, or space in which they are placed.

The Treble or G clef  which encircles the second line, establishes the note G on this line, from which

the other lines and spaces are named as follows:

G   A   B   C   D   E   F   G   G   F   E   D

In addition notes are written upon and between short lines above and below the staff. These lines are called leger lines.

G   A   B   C   D   D   C   B   A   G   F   E

Every   Good   Boy   Does   Finely   F - A - C - E

A rest indicates a pause, or silence for the value of the note after which it is named, such as

Semibreve Rest   Minim Rests   Crotchet Rests   Quaver Rests

The end of the piece is indicated by a light and heavy line

When a section or part of a piece is to be repeated it will be shown by a double bar with two dots.

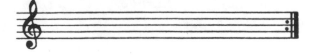

PARTS OF THE CLARINET

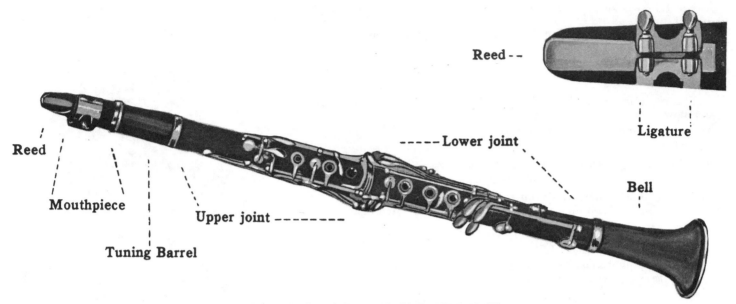

CARE OF THE INSTRUMENT

Your clarinet will not sound its best, nor will your learning to play it be easy unless everything pertaining to the instrument is kept in perfect condition. This applies to mouthpiece, reed, keys, pads, springs, etc. Any one of these not in perfect condition will greatly handicap your playing.

THE MOUTHPIECE, one of the most important parts of your instrument should be of good quality and be tested by your teacher before using.

THE REED should be selected with utmost care. One of medium soft texture is best for the young player. Too hard or too soft reeds will make it impossible to produce a good tone. BE SURE TO THOROUGHLY MOISTEN THE REED BEFORE USING. The reed should be held firmly, but not too tightly by the ligature. Your teacher will show you how to " set " the reed.

After playing, remove reed from mouthpiece and wipe moisture from both parts. Replace but do not clamp too tightly. Put on cap. BE SURE TO HAVE EXTRA REEDS ON HAND.

THE KEYS on your clarinet are a very delicate piece of mechanism and should not be bent or thrown out of alignment. A drop of light oil should be applied to screws and springs from time to time.

WOODEN CLARINETS should receive special care. Consult with your teacher regarding cleaning and oiling.

BE SURE TO GREASE THE CORK JOINTS WHENEVER NECESSARY.

Take pride in the way your instrument looks by keeping it bright and clean.

FAILURE ON YOUR PART IN NOT REGULARLY FOLLOWING OUT THE ABOVE INSTRUCTIONS IN REGARD TO THE CARE OF YOUR INSTRUMENT WILL RESULT IN EXPENSIVE REPAIR COSTS.

FOREWORD TO STUDENTS

No student should attempt the study of an instrument without the aid of a competent instructor for that particular instrument.

Due to the variations of mouth, teeth, and lip formations of different individuals, I believe the all important questions as to position of mouthpiece, breathing, tongueing, and lip control should be decided by your teacher for your particular case.

TECHNICAL

The most important technical points for wind instrument players are as follow

(1) Developing and strengthening the lip muscles.
   (*Process*)   Playing of long sustained notes.

(2) Developing clarity and precision in attacks.
   (*Process*)   Proper use of the tongue.

(3) Developing a fine quality of tone.
   (*Process*)   A combination of No. 1 and careful listening.

(4) Developing fluency in fingering.
   (*Process*)   Playing of scales and arpeggios in various keys.

(5) Developing a mastery of the entire range of the instrument.
   (*Process*)   A combination of all of the above.

CORRECT POSITION (POSTURE)

When playing the clarinet always stand or sit erect with the head up. Arms, hands and fingers should be completely relaxed and held in a natural position. Any stiffness of the body will be reflected in the quality of your playing. Fig. 1. When practising, it is better to play in a standing position as this will help you to breathe properly.

LES BROWN
Popular Orchestra Leader—OKEH Records
Photo—Courtesy C. G. Conn, Ltd.

HOLDING AND FINGERING THE CLARINET

The clarinet is balanced and supported in position by the first joint of the RIGHT thumb, which should press slightly upward against the thumb rest. The fingers of the RIGHT hand are used for the holes and keys of the LOWER part of the instrument. The LEFT hand thumb is used for the thumb hole (T) and the register key (R). The fingers of the LEFT hand are used for the holes and keys of the UPPER part of the clarinet. The fingers should be curved slightly to permit the fleshy part of the first joint to cover the holes.

EMBOUCHURE
(*How to hold mouthpiece and reed in the mouth*)

Turn the lower lip in over the lower teeth so that the teeth rest under the edge of the red part of the lip. Place the mouthpiece in the mouth with the reed resting against the lower lip and about one-half inch of the reed inside the mouth. To ensure that the mouthpiece enters the mouth at the proper angle the right thumb, when on the thumb rest of the clarinet, should be about six inches from the body when the player is in an erect standing or sitting position. As the upper teeth come to rest gently, but firmly on the top of the mouthpiece, seal the lips about the mouthpiece and pull the corners of the mouth slightly outward as when smiling. Place the tongue against the reed about a quarter of an inch from its tip, and about the same distance from the tip of the reed. When the breath is started from the diaphragm, remove the tongue from the reed with the same action as when pronouncing the syllable " ti ", and allow the breath to flow into the instrument in a steady stream. DO NOT PUFF CHEEKS. Each note should be started with the above tongue action except that between consecutive notes the breath remains constant, and the notes are separated by the touch of the tongue on the reed. Be sure to moisten the reed thoroughly before playing.

TUNING YOUR INSTRUMENT

Clarinets are pitched in B♭, which means that when you read and finger C, the actual pitch sounding is B♭, thus the PIANO must play one whole tone lower than the note you are fingering. The tuning barrel may be drawn out to lower the pitch of the instrument.

PHRASING

The breath marks ('), in addition to indicating the proper places to breathe, also serve as an introduction to the feeling of proper phrasing of melodies. This is important as it is that which gives meaning to music.

HOW TO PRACTISE

The most important part of your practising is in being able to think out the problems at hand, fingering, tongueing, phrasing, etc. WHAT YOU CAN'T THINK YOU CAN'T PLAY. Be sure to do a good piece of work on lesson 1 before attempting lesson 2, and so on with each succeeding lesson. Play slowly at first and think carefully the rhythm (note values) phrasing, tone, fingering and attack (tongueing). YOU are your own best teacher. Learn to intelligently criticise your own playing. I believe you know when you have done a good job and when you haven't. Don't be satisfied with a lesson half done, you are only fooling yourself. A good student is one who practises regularly every day. DO YOU?

DIAGRAM OF FINGERING

LOW REGISTER

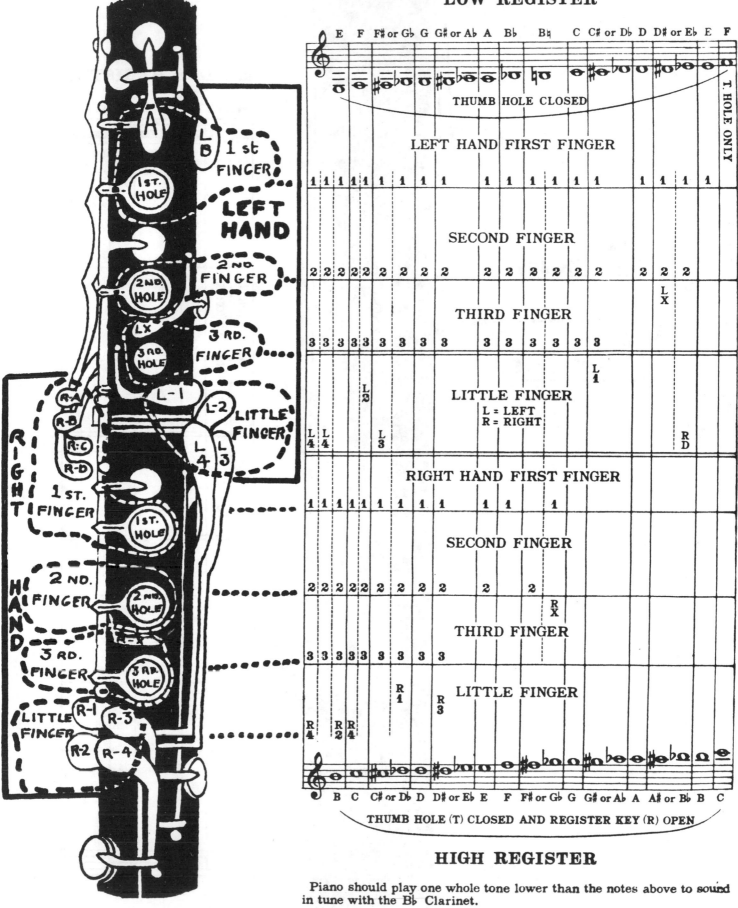

Piano should play one whole tone lower than the notes above to sound in tune with the Bb Clarinet.

HIGH REGISTER

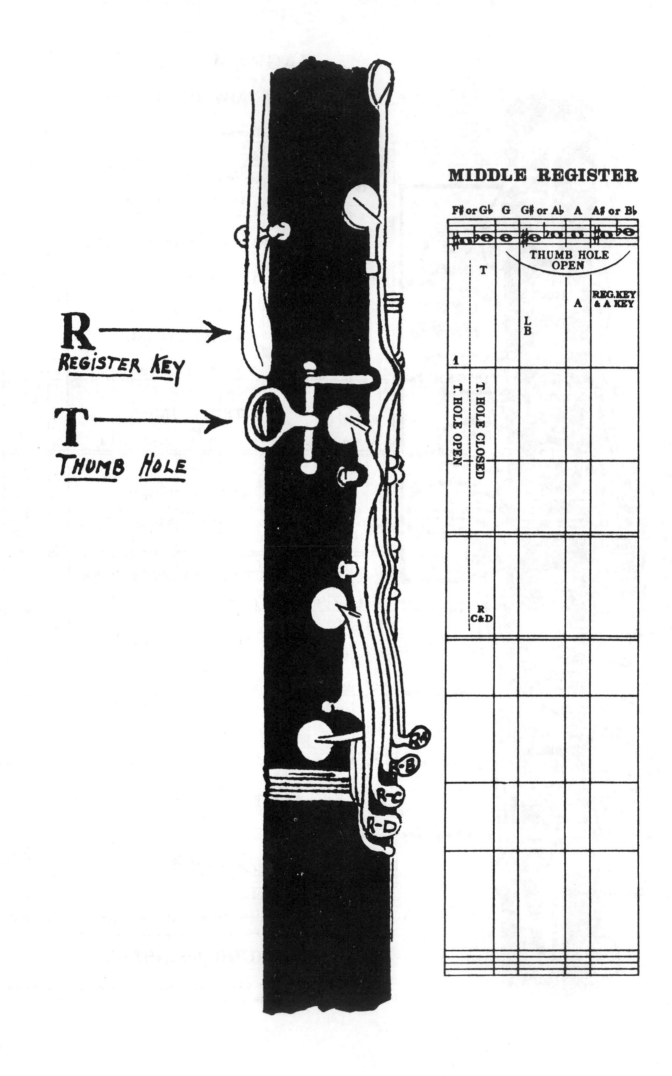

R → REGISTER KEY

T → THUMB HOLE

MIDDLE REGISTER

F♯ or G♭	G	G♯ or A♭	A	A♯ or B♭
	T	THUMB HOLE OPEN		
			A	REG. KEY & A KEY
		L B		
1				
T. HOLE OPEN	T. HOLE CLOSED			
	R C&D			

A TUNE A DAY

LESSON 1

OBJECTIVES: 1. To learn the correct habits of
    (a) Posture.
    (b) Holding the clarinet.
    (c) Position of mouthpiece.
    (d) Breathing and production of tone.
2. To correlate the keys and holes of the clarinet
with the note E on the staff.
3. To know the value of minims, crotchets and rests.

MINIMS (2 Count) Notes   and MINIM (2 Count) Rests

Introducing 1st line E.
Played with the left hand
thumb & 1st finger hole.

THUMB HOLE CLOSED

LEFT HAND

This note is E and is played T. I.

① Think Count: 1 2 3 4

② This note is ____? Think Count: 1 2 3 4

CROTCHETS (1 Count) Notes   and CROTCHET (1 Count) Rests

③ Think Count: 1 2 3 4

④ These are _____ and receive ____ count?

Minims and Crotchets
Beethoven
(From Seventh Symphony)

Adapted

Pupil

⑤ Count: 1 2 3 4

Teacher**

* Attack each note firmly. (>)

** Advanced students may also play the teacher parts in all lessons.

LESSON 1A

OBJECTIVES:
1. Continuation of the objectives of lesson 1.
2. To learn the meaning of the TIE (⌣)
3. To learn the name and fingering for the notes D and C.
4. To learn the meaning of the breath mark. (')

Introducing 1st space below the staff D. Played with the left hand thumb and 1st & 2nd finger holes.

THUMB HOLE CLOSED

LEFT HAND

⑥ Think Count: 1 2 3 4

⑦ This note is _____
Think Count: 1 2 3 4

⑧ Think Count: 1 2 3 4

⑨ These are _____ and receive ___ count?
Think Count: 1 2 3 4

Little D and E March

This mark (') indicates the breathing places.

Pupil
⑩
Teacher

This note is _____

Introducing 1st line below the staff C.
Played with the thumb and 1st, 2nd & 3rd
finger holes.

⑪ This note is _____?

Think Count: 1 2 3 4

THUMB HOLE CLOSED   **LEFT HAND**

⑫ These are _____?

Think Count: 1 2 3 4

Merrily

Pupil

⑬

Teacher

1   2   3   4

This note is _____

*When two notes on the same degree (line or space) of the staff are tied by a slur ⌢ they are to be played as one note, adding the value of the two notes together.

LESSON 2

OBJECTIVES: 1. Application of acquired knowledge by the playing of melodies.
2. Learning to feel the rhythm of minims and crotchets.
3. Do home work assignment.

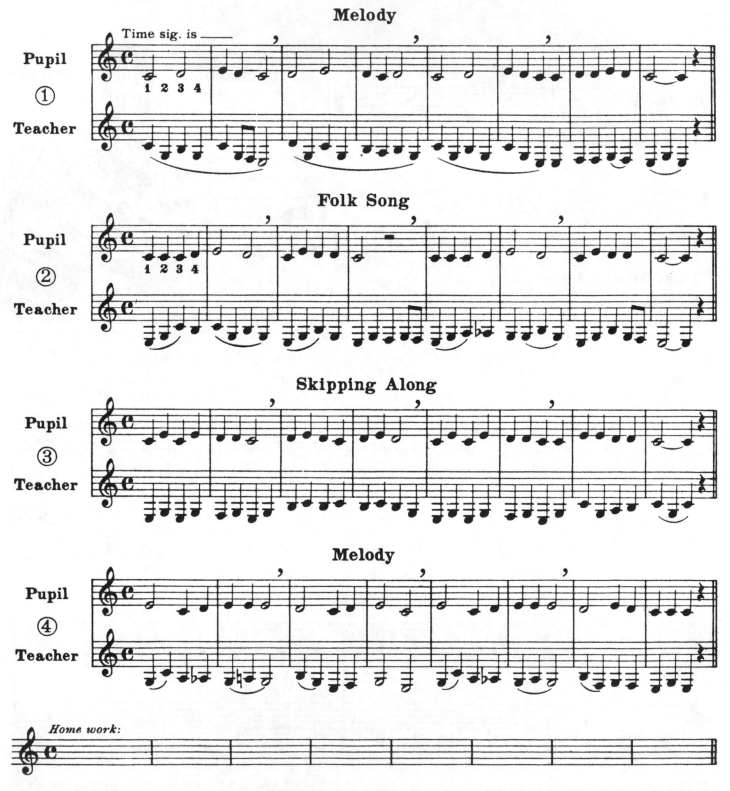

Home work: Write line of notes thus far studied using minims and crotchets. Mark the letter name (C-D-E) above each note.

OBJECTIVES:
1. To learn the name and fingering for first space F.
2. Further practice with minims, crotchets and rests.
3. Answer questions and do home work assignment.

LESSON 4

6

OBJECTIVES:
1. To learn the name and fingering for 2nd line G.
2. To learn the proper use of the right hand thumb in supporting the clarinet.
3. Application of acquired knowledge by the playing of familiar melodies.
4. Questions and home work in this and following lessons.

Introducing 2nd line G. Played open (no fingers) Have right hand thumb keep a firm upward pressure. To make it easier to hold the clarinet while playing this note you may use this fingering.

THUMB HOLE OPEN   LEFT HAND

Skips

Oats and Beans

Jingle Bells

Home work: Write line of notes thus far studied.
Divide into bars using minims and crotchets.

LESSON 4A

OBJECTIVES: 1. To learn the value of semibreves and semibreve rests.
2. Emphasis on rhythm. (note values)
3. The playing of Duets and Trios. (Practise all parts)

* *Simile* - To continue as before.

LESSON 5

OBJECTIVES: 1. To learn the name and fingering for 2nd space A.
2. Application of acquired knowledge by the playing of familiar and unfamiliar melodies.

Introducing 2nd space A.
Played with the side of the left hand first finger. Use a rolling motion. Thumb hole open.

A key

A

THUMB HOLE OPEN

A KEY

A

LEFT HAND

① Think Count: 1 2 3 4

② These are _____ and receive _____ counts?
Think Count: 1 2 3 4   *simile*

③

Folk Song
(Trio)

④ Pupil — NEW NOTE

Pupil — THINK

Teacher

B

Twinkle, Twinkle, Little Star

⑤ This note is _____
Think Count: 1 2 3 4

The Boat Song

Unfamiliar Melody — test

Think fingering and note values

⑥ 1 2 3 4

C. P. H.

LESSON 5A
Slurred Notes (*legato)

OBJECTIVES: 1. To learn the meaning of legato. (slurred notes)
2. Slurring notes in groups of 2-4 and 8.
3. Application of this knowledge in the playing of a
   familiar melody.

This sign (⌢ slur) when placed above or below two or more notes indicates that they are to be played in one breath, and that only the first notes of each group should be tongued.

Lightly Row

*Smoothly - connected

TEST QUESTIONS ON LESSONS 1-5

Questions from this, and following test-sheets, will be given as a check on your home-study of preceding lessons.

REMEMBER: The more you know and understand about the signs and symbols used in music-writing, the easier it will be for you to learn how to play well.

		Points	Your score
(1)	This ▭ is called? _____	5	....
(2)	This symbol 𝄞 is called? _____	5	....
(3)	The staff is divided by bar-lines into? _____	5	....
(4)	Fractions at the beginning of music are called _____ signatures?	5	....
(5)	This 𝄞 is a _____ and has _____ counts?	4	....
(6)	These 𝄞 are _____ and have _____ counts each?	4	....
(7)	These 𝄞 are _____ and have _____ count each?	4	....
(8)	Lines and spaces are named after the first _____ letters of the alphabet?	5	....
(9)	This 𝄞 is a _____ rest?	4	....
(10)	These 𝄞 are _____ rests?	4	....
(11)	These 𝄞 are _____ rests?	4	....
(12)	This sign 𝄞 means _____ counts to each bar:	5	....
(13)	Name the notes thus far studied. _____	6	....
(14)	Write the notes thus far studied. 𝄞	6	....
(15)	Write the letter names above the following notes.	6	....
(16)	Divide the following into bars.	6	....
(17)	Inspection of instrument.	10	....
(18)	Sight reading.	12	....
		100	

TEACHER: Write line of notes thus far studied, using semibreves, minims and crotchets as a sight reading test.

OBJECTIVES: 1. To learn the name and fingering for 1st space F#.
                 2. To learn the use of an alternate fingering for this new note.
                 3. To learn the meaning of the sharp. (#)

Introducing 1st space F sharp. (F#)
Played with the 1st finger hole covered.
Note that the thumb hole is open. Note
also the alternate fingering for this
note, see Ex. 3.

A SHARP (#) RAISES THE NOTE TO WHICH IT.
APPLIES BY A SEMITONE.

A NATURAL (♮) TAKES AWAY THE EFFECT OF A
SHARP OR FLAT AND RESTORES THE NOTE TO
ITS ORIGINAL PITCH.

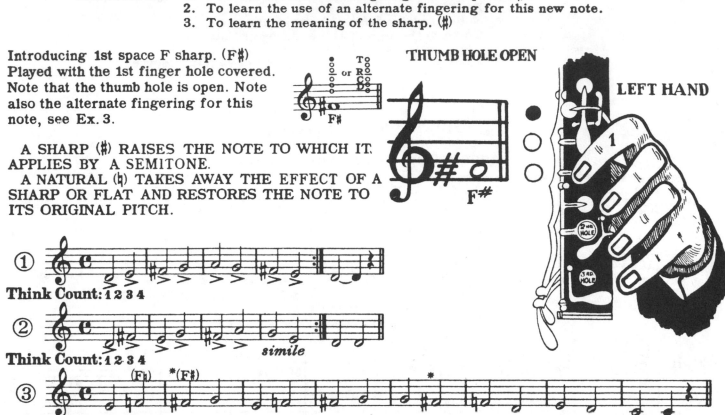

Think Count: 1 2 3 4

Think Count: 1 2 3 4

Think Count: 1 2 3 4

*When F# is written between F♮ & G use the following fingering for F#. Use the thumb hole plus the two lower side keys (R-C & D) played with the first finger of the right hand.

The Key of G Major (one sharp (#) F#)

The sharp (#) placed on the top line of the staff, just after the clef sign, affects every F throughout the piece, except when temporarily cancelled by a natural (♮) sign. NOTICE KEY SIGNATURES AND FINGER ACCORDINGLY.

Old English

Think Count: 1 2 3 4

Lightly Row

Think Count: 1 2 3 4

Review the above melody in lesson 5A in the key of C.

Abide With Me

Monk

Home work: Mark the letter name below all notes in Ex. 4, 5 and 6.

LESSON 7

OBJECTIVES:
1. Application of acquired knowledge through the playing of DUETS. (practise both parts)
2. Notice key signatures and what they mean.
3. To learn the keys of C (no sharps or flats) and D. (two sharps, F & C sharp)
4. Learning to hear intervals, difference in pitch between two notes.

Duets (Practise Both Parts)

Upidee (Key of C—No sharps (♯) or flats (♭))

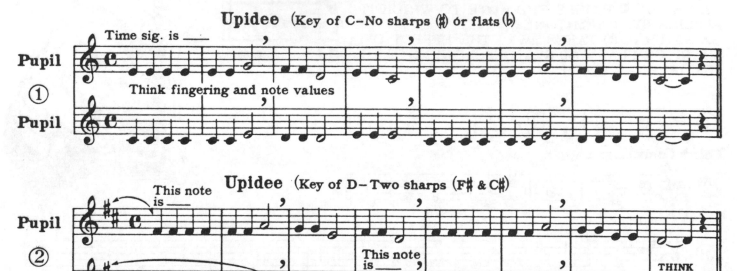

Upidee (Key of D—Two sharps (F♯ & C♯))

Merrily (Key of ____ the sharps are ____)

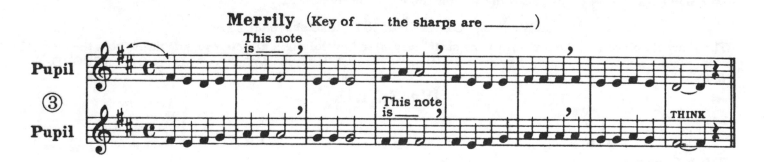

Au clair de la lune (Key of ____)

OBJECTIVES: 1. To learn the name and fingering for low B natural. (B♮)
2. Continuation of legato playing.
3. To learn the importance of practising long notes.

Introducing low B♮.
Played with the thumb and three fingers of the left hand plus the second finger of the right hand.

THUMB HOLE CLOSED

Folk Song

Melody

This exercise is not easy. Practise it carefully until you can play it smoothly.

DON'T FORGET YOUR DAILY PRACTICE ON LONG NOTES. ONLY IN THIS WAY CAN YOU GAIN BREATH CONTROL, LIP DEVELOPMENT AND A FINE QUALITY OF TONE.

LESSON 9

OBJECTIVES: 1. To learn the names and fingerings for low A and G.
2. Continued emphasis on rhythm and fingering.
3. Application of acquired knowledge.

Introducing low A.
Played with the thumb
and five finger holes.

Preparation

① ② ③

Skips on Intervals*

④

Russian Folk Song

⑤

*An interval is the difference in pitch between two notes. Intervals are counted from the lowest note to the highest.

Introducing low G.
Played with the thumb
and six finger holes.

Evening Song

Schumann

Think Count: 1 2 3 4

LESSON 10

OBJECTIVES: 1. To learn the formation of the natural scale.
(Placement of whole-tones and semitones)
2. To play the G Major scale and arpeggio. (from memory)
3. Playing melodies in the key of G. (think F♯)
4. To learn the meaning of staccato. (the dot (·) Ex. 5.

The Scale

A scale is a succession of notes from a given key-note to its octave, 8 notes higher. The form on which all major scales are modelled is as follows:

The Natural, or C Major Scale
No sharps or flats

The ascending progression is: two whole tones, one semitone, three whole tones, one semitone. The semitones come between the numbers 3-4, 7-8.

Scale of G Major
One Sharp, F♯. Semitones B to C, & F♯ to G.

Beneath Thy Guiding Hand

J. Hatton

Observe slurs carefully

From the Second Symphony

Haydn

Key of____ The sharp is____ Time sig. is____

THINK

This note is ____

Home work: Learn to play the G Major Scale from memory.

*A dot (·) above or below a note indicates that the note is to be played short, about half it's regular value. For explanation see page 30.

TEST QUESTIONS ON LESSONS 6-10

		Points	Your score

(1)   This sign 𝄆: means? _____   4   ....

(2)   This (♯) is a? _____   4   ....

(3)   How does a (♯) affect a note? _____   4   ....

(4)   This (♮) is a? _____   4   ....

(5)   How does a (♮) affect a note? _____   4   ....

(6)   Name the following lines and spaces of the staff?   8   ....

     1st space _____   2nd space _____
     3rd space _____   1st line _____
     3rd line _____   2nd line _____
     1st line below staff _____   1st space below staff _____

(7)   The key of (2♯) is? _____   4   ....

(8)   Write the key signature of (2♯)   4   ....

(9)   This sign ⌒ connecting two or more notes means? _____   4   ....

(10)   **What is a scale?** _____   6   ....

(11)   Write the G major scale.   8   ....

(12)   The key of (1♯) is? _____   4   ....

(13)   Write the key signature of (1♯)   4   ....

(14)   This note ___ is? _____   4   ....

(15)   This note ___ is? _____   4   ....

(16)   This note ___ is? _____   4   ....

(17)   Music written for two clarinets is called? _____   6   ....

(18)   Inspection of instrument.   10   ....

(19)   Sight reading.   10   ....

                                                     100

TEACHER: Write line of notes thus far studied using slurs.

LESSON 11

OBJECTIVES: 1. To learn the value of the quaver.
2. To learn the use of rhythms involving quavers in $\frac{4}{4}$ and $\frac{2}{4}$ time.
3. To learn the meaning of D.S. (Dal Segno.)

Quavers

A quaver (♪) is equal to half the value of a crotchet. Two quavers (♫) equal one crotchet, four ♫♫ a minim, and eight ♫♫♫♫ a semibreve. A quaver-rest (⌐) is equal to the value of a quaver.

$\frac{2}{4}$ TIME MEANS { Two counts to a bar. A crotchet gets one count.

Comparison of $\frac{4}{4}$ with $\frac{2}{4}$ time

One bar of $\frac{4}{4}$ time equals two bars of $\frac{2}{4}$ time.

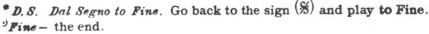

*D.S. Dal Segno to Fine. Go back to the sign (𝄋) and play to Fine.

⁾Fine — the end.

Supplementary Material

Theme from Symphony No. 1

Brahms

Slowly

Think Count: 4   1 2 3 4

God Save The Queen*

1 2 & 3

1   2 & 3 &

Andante
(from Surprise Symphony)

Haydn

Slowly

Reuben and Rachel

Note time signature

THINK

Melody
(Duet)

Haydn

Pupil

Teacher

P.

T.

* Although ¾ rhythm has not been introduced up to this lesson, this well known melody is given here as a challenge to the pupil.

LESSON 12

OBJECTIVES: 1. To learn a new rhythm ($\frac{3}{4}$ time, with emphasis on the rhythm drills). (A-B-C-etc.)
2. To learn the value and use of dotted crotchets and dotted minims.

The Dotted Minim and the Dotted Crotchet

A dot is equal to one half the value of the note it follows. A dotted minim equals 3 beats, a dotted crotchet equals $1\frac{1}{2}$ beats.

Rhythm Drills

Count aloud each variation while clapping the hands once for each note. Repeat several times until you feel the rhythm before playing. Variation (F) is the most difficult and should be thoroughly understood.

Combination of Rhythms in $\frac{3}{4}$ time

Think Count: 1 2 3

Home work:

Home work: Write 8 bars of notes thus far studied, using different groupings of notes in $\frac{3}{4}$ time.

LESSON 13

OBJECTIVES:
1. Application of $\frac{3}{4}$ and $\frac{2}{4}$ rhythm through familiar melodies in different keys.
2. Knowledge of first- and second-time bars (Ex. 2)
3. Learning to play melodies from memory.
4. Knowledge of the up beat. (Ex. 2)
5. Knowledge of musical terms of tempo. (speed)

Brightly (Allegretto) **French Folk Song**

Key of ____ sharp is ____ Time sig. is ____

Think Count: 1 2 3

THINK

First- and Second-Time Bars

The term 1st and 2nd time bars applies to one or more bars in brackets at a double bar; thus when the strain is repeated, the first ending is omitted and the second ending played instead.

The Up-Beat

Many pieces begin with an incomplete bar, usually starting with the last beat or fraction thereof. This is called the up-beat. The ending always completes the bar of the up-beat.

Rather slowly (Andante) **Home on the Range** Cowboy Song

Key of ____ Time sig. is ____

UP BEAT

1. FIRST TIME BAR

Think Count: 3   1 2 3

2. SECOND TIME BAR

Moderate speed (Moderato) **College Song**

Key of ____ Time sig. is ____

Think Count: 1 2 &   1 2 &

Andante **Melody** Beethoven

Key of ____ Time sig. is ____

Think Count:

Observe slurs carefully

Home work: Learn to play one of the above melodies from memory.

LESSON 14

OBJECTIVES:
1. To learn the name and fingering for 3rd line B♭.
2. To learn the meaning of the flat. (♭)
3. To learn the meaning of the accidental. (F♯ in Ex.5)
4. To learn the meaning of the key of F Major.

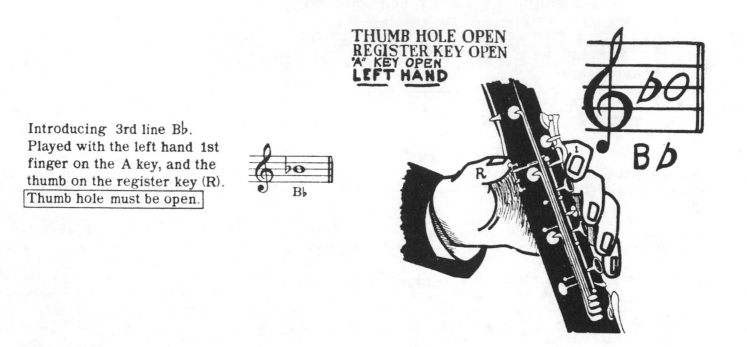

THUMB HOLE OPEN
REGISTER KEY OPEN
"A" KEY OPEN
LEFT HAND

Introducing 3rd line B♭.
Played with the left hand 1st finger on the A key, and the thumb on the register key (R).

Thumb hole must be open.

B♭

B♭

Key of F Major

A flat (♭) lowers the pitch of a note by a semitone (half step).

Key of F Major, one flat (♭), B♭. The flat (♭) placed on the third line of the staff, just after the clef sign, affects every B throughout the piece.

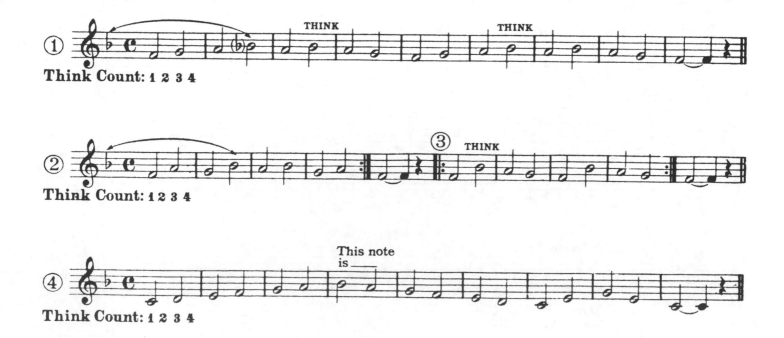

① Think Count: 1 2 3 4

② Think Count: 1 2 3 4

④ Think Count: 1 2 3 4

Lesson 14 continued on next page.

Accidentals

An accidental is a sharp or flat which does not appear in the key signature. They apply ONLY to the bar in which they are placed. See Ex. 5, the F♯ in bars 3 and 7.

Go Down Moses

Andante

Think Count: 4   1   2   3   4

Yankee Doodle

Moderato

Key of ____ The flat is ____ Time sig. is ____

Think Count: 1   &   2   &

Hymn

Andante

Key of ____ The flat is ____ Time sig. is ____

Haydn

Think Count: 1   1   2   3   4

Home work:

Home work: Write line of notes thus far studied, using semibreves, minims and crotchets. Mark the letter names below.

LESSON 15

OBJECTIVES: 1. Application of acquired knowledge by playing familiar Christmas melodies.

2. Knowledge of the pause-Fermata. (⌢)

Theme From "Lobgesang"

Mendelssohn

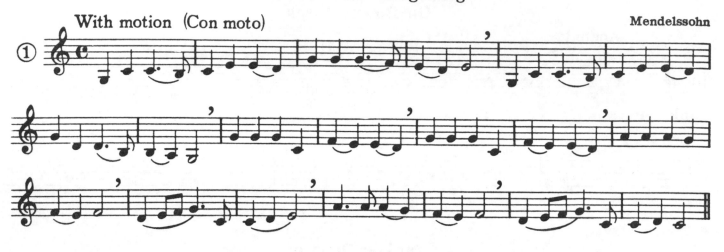

We Three Kings of Orient Are

Hopkins

The First Noël

Home work: Learn to play one of the above melodies from memory.

* ⌢ Pause (**fermata**) a short curved line drawn over a dot, prolongs the time of the note.

TEST QUESTIONS ON LESSONS 11-15

		Points	Your score
(1)	These 𝄞 ♩♩♩♩ are _____ ?	5	....
(2)	Each of the above notes in 4/4 or 2/4 time receives _____ count	5	....
(3)	This 𝄞 𝅗𝅥. is a _____ ?	5	....
(4)	The above note has _____ counts?	5	....
(5)	This 𝄞 ♩. 𝄽 is a _____ ?	5	....
(6)	The above note has _____ counts?	5	....
(7)	Divide the following into bars?	5	....

4/4 ♩ ♫♩ ♫♫♩ ♩ ‖ 3/4 𝅗𝅥. ♫♩ ♩. ♪♩ ‖ 2/4 ♫♩ ♩ 𝅗𝅥 ♫♩ ‖

| (8) | Mark the count under the following? | 5 | .... |

2/4 ♩ ♫♩|♫♩ ♩‖ 3/4 𝅗𝅥. ♪♩|♩ ♫♩|‖ 4/4 𝅗𝅥. ♪♫♩|♫♫♩ ♩|♫♩‖

(9)	This 𝄇 means?_____	5	....
(10)	This sign ⌢ means?_____	2	....
(11)	What is meant by the (up-beat)? _____	5	....
(12)	This (♭) is a?_____	2	....
(13)	How does a (♭) affect a note?_____	3	....
(14)	The name of this note 𝄞 ♭𝅝 is?_____	3	....
(15)	The key of (1♭) is? _____	5	....
(16)	Write the key signature of (1♭) 𝄞	5	....
(17)	What is the meaning of D. S. (Dal Segno)?_____	5	....
(18)	What is the meaning of 2/4 time?_____	5	....
(19)	What is an accidental?_____	5	....
(20)	What is the meaning of Andante _____ Allegretto? _____	5	....
(21)	Sight reading.	10 / 100	....

𝄞 3/4 _____

TEACHER: Write line of notes using different rhythm patterns in 3/4 time.

LESSON 16

OBJECTIVES:
1. To learn the name and fingering for low Bb.
2. To learn the use of an alternate fingering for B♮
3. The playing of familiar and unfamiliar melodies using low Bb.

Introducing low Bb.
Played with the thumb and four finger holes. Note substitute fingering for B♮ in Ex. 2.

THUMB HOLE
CLOSED   LEFT HAND

RIGHT HAND

* When B♮ precedes or follows Bb use the following fingering for B♮. Use the regular Bb fingering plus the little key R+ between the second and third holes of the right hand. Use 3rd finger for this key.

Merrily

Familiar melodies
(Listen carefully)

French Folk Song

Key of ____ flats are ____

Harvest Time

Unfamiliar melody (test)
Think Bb and note values

C. P. H.

Andante (Slowly)   **Duet**

von Weber

Key of ____

Pupil

Practise both parts

Pupil

OBJECTIVES: 1. To learn the name and fingering for low F.
                 2. To learn the value and importance of firm finger action.
                 3. Playing the F Major scale and arpeggio. (lower octave.)

Introducing low F.
Played with the thumb,
six finger holes and R-4.

THUMB HOLE CLOSED

Press fingers firmly   NEW NOTE

Press fingers firmly

Scale and Arpeggio of F Major (lower octave)
Semitones A to B♭ and E to F.

(THINK B♭)

THINK

Key of ___ Time sig. is ___

Holy, Holy, Holy

Moderato   Dykes
Key of ___ flat is ___ Time sig. is ___

THINK

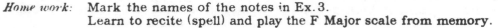

Home work: Mark the names of the notes in Ex. 3.
                   Learn to recite (spell) and play the F Major scale from memory.

LESSON 18

OBJECTIVES: 1. To learn the name and fingering for low E.
2. Correlation of notes in the lower register, (name and position on staff) with proper fingering.
3. Playing familiar melodies involving the use of Quavers in $\frac{4}{4}$ and $\frac{3}{4}$ time.

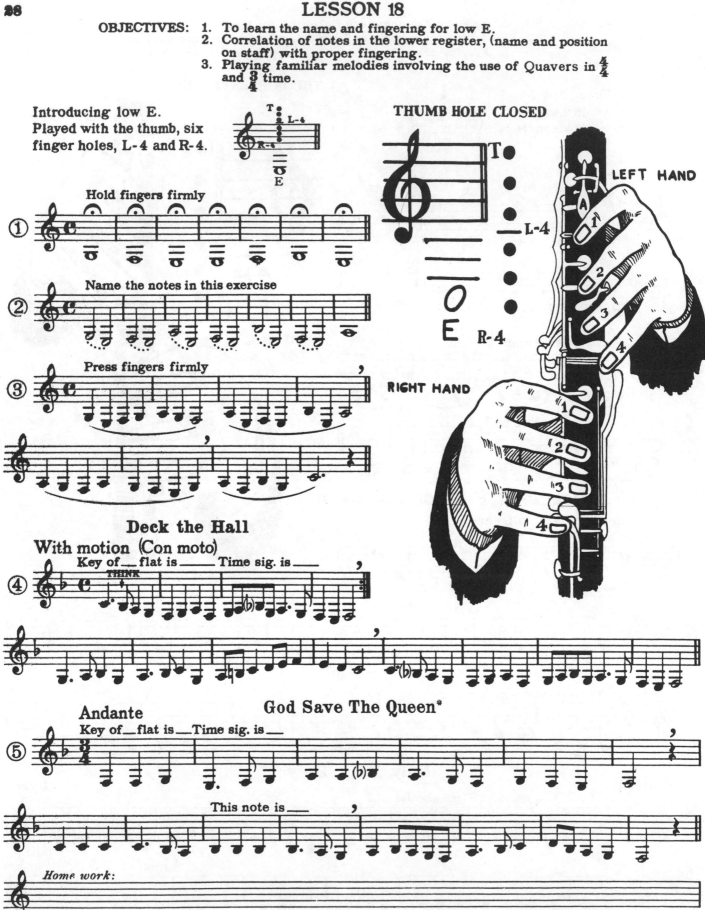

Introducing low E.
Played with the thumb, six finger holes, L-4 and R-4.

THUMB HOLE CLOSED

LEFT HAND

RIGHT HAND

① Hold fingers firmly

② Name the notes in this exercise

③ Press fingers firmly

Deck the Hall

With motion (Con moto)

④ Key of __ flat is ____ Time sig. is ____

God Save The Queen*

Andante

⑤ Key of __ flat is __ Time sig. is __

This note is __

Home work:

*Try to play this air in the key of C by ear. Hear the next note and sense the fingering. Starts on C.
Home work: Learn to play teacher parts to duets in Lessons 2 and 3. Write line of notes studied below middle C. Divide into bars and mark time signature. Use minims, crotchets and quavers.

Music for Schools

A specially selected range of music books, tutors and reference books for schools and libraries.
From folk to pop, jazz to classics, every book is graded according to age and ability.

The Complete Guitar Player
by Russ Shipton
For classroom or private use. Easy to follow text with diagrams and demonstration photographs. Special bands of colour focus the attention of the guitarist on the music. All songs or solos are on one page or facing pages. Most of the course is based on the music of modern performers such as Bob Dylan, John Denver and The Beatles. Enables you to play right from lesson one to an advanced stage, and assumes you have no knowledge of music.
Book 1, also contains pull-out chord chart and unique tuning record. *(CD), AM 25123*
Book 2 *(CD), AM 25131*
Book 3 *(CD), AM 25149*
Book 4 *(CD), AM 25156*
Complete set of separate books also available. *AM 25164*

The Complete Guitar Player
Omnibus Edition Books 1, 2, 3, and 4 *(CD), AM 26691*

The Complete Guitar Player Cassettes
Four cassettes in all, one to each book of The Complete Guitar Player.
Cassette: Book 1 *(CD), OM 20004*
Cassette: Book 2 *(CD), OM 20012*
Cassette: Book 3 *(CD), OM 20038*
Cassette: Book 4 *(CD), OM 20046*

The Complete Guitar Player Chord Book
by Russ Shipton
Shows exactly what chords are needed to both play and arrange songs. Many clear photographs plus unique demonstration record.
(CD), AM 31717

Chord Book Cassette
This cassette supplements the contents of 'The Complete Guitar Player Chord Book'.
(CD), OM 20137

Key to Grading (C) 13-16 years
(A) 5-8 years   (D) 17 and above
(B) 9-12 years   (t) with teacher
Example: (Bt) means suitable for
9-12 year old working with teacher.

The Complete Guitar Player Video
Full colour teaching video lasting 60 minutes which is an important addition to The Complete Guitar Player series. A self-contained home study course.
VHS *(CD), OV 10002*
Beta *(CD), OV 10010*

The Complete Rock & Pop Guitar Player
Learn to play guitar in the style of Dire Straits, Duran Duran, Bruce Springsteen . . . right from lesson one. Easy-to-follow lessons, diagrams and demonstration photographs.
Book 1
Holding your guitar, tuning, chord changing. Pull out chord chart.
(CD), AM 60278
Book 2
Easy musical notation, tablature, rock and reggae strum patterns. Classic backing riffs, new chords.
(CD), AM 60286
Book 3
Introduction to harmony, new chords, arpeggio style accompaniment, modern rhythm styles, strumming effects.
(CD), AM 60294
Book 4
Electronic effects, new chords and backing styles, hammer-ons and pull-offs, new riffs, advanced techniques.
(CD), AM 60302

D.I.Y. Guitar Repair
by Pieter J. Fillet
Easy-to-follow instructions, plus 170 diagrams and photos. Slim format.
(CD), AM 38530

Guitar Case Chord Book
by Peter Pickow
Fits into your guitar case. Clear readable diagrams and no page flipping.
(CD), AM 35841

The Guitarist's Picture Chords
by Happy Traum
The most useful guitar chords in every key diagrammed in three different positions. The first position is accompanied by a photograph.
(CD), AM 16015

The Guitarist's Picture Chord Encyclopedia
by John Pearse
Every chord you'll ever need to play shown in photographs, diagrams and standard notation.
(CD), OP 41797

Instant Guitar: Play Today
Fastest way to learn guitar. Written in easy to follow language, it assumes no knowledge of music. Instructional record included.
(CD), AM 32517

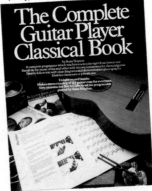

The Complete Guitar Player Classical Book
by Russ Shipton
The complete method clearly explained in text and many demonstration photographs. A collection of tunes to play.
(CD), AM 38217

Solo Guitar Playing
by Frederick Noad
Instruction, including graded exercises, practice studies and a survey of the guitar repertoire etc.
(BD), OK 61994

Solo Guitar Playing Book 2
by Frederick Noad
Technique, sight-reading, musicianship for the intermediate guitarist. Plus graded exercises and practice studies and an advanced repertoire of thirty works.
(BD), OP 40591

Accompanying Tapes to Solo Guitar Playing
by Frederick Noad
Tape A: Exercises & Study Pieces, Page 43–Page 128.
(BD), OM20236.
Tape B: Exercises & Study Pieces, Page 130–Page 213.
(BD), OM20244
Double Cassette: Pack A & B.
(BD), OM20293

Tuning Your Guitar
by Donald Brosnac
Fits into your guitar case. Easy-to-follow text and diagrams – will do wonders even for the so-called 'tone deaf'.
(CD), AM 35858

Using Your Guitar
by Brook Hedick
Fits into your guitar case. Basic instruction, maintaining your guitar, tablature and song accompaniment etc. are some of the points covered in this comprehensive book.
(CD), AM 35783

Songbooks with Guitar & Piano Accompaniments

The Beatles Complete: Guitar
(I), NO 17303

The Beatles Complete (Revised)
Guitar/Vocal: Melody line chord boxes and symbols, 388pp.
(I), NO 18145

The Complete Guitar Player Songbook
Contains all the songs and music featured in The Complete Guitar Player. In standard notation with diagrams and chord symbols plus full lyrics.
(EI), AM 26527

The Complete Guitar Player Songbook No.2
This new book contains 50 songs which are arranged in keys which are examined in 'The Complete Guitar Player' books. Includes chords, left hand fingerings and right hand rhythm pattern, also lyrics.
(EI), AM 31634.

The Complete Guitar Player Songbook No.3
Another 50 songs by Paul McCartney, The Rolling Stones, Buddy Holly etc. In standard notation with chord boxes and full lyrics. Useful references to The Complete Guitar Player Course are printed with each song.
(EI), AM 33291

The Complete Guitar Player Songbook No.4
Of special interest to players who have followed The Complete Guitar Player Course. 50 songs by Billy Joel, John Denver, Elvis Presley etc. Standard notation, chord boxes and full lyrics.
(EI), AM 33754

The Complete Guitar Player Songbook No.5
Fifty songs by David Bowie, Bob Marley, The Police and many others in standard notation with chord boxes and full lyrics.
(EI), AM 38027

The Complete Guitar Player Songbook No.6
Songs from Elvis Costello, Sting, Mark Knopfler and other stars. Fifty numbers in standard notation with chord boxes and lyrics.
(EI), AM 38209

Animal Songs For Children
More than 40 animal songs beloved by children the world over. Melody lines in standard notation with chord names. New piano accompaniment.
(E), AM 60062

The Beatles Complete: Piano/Vocal, Easy Organ
Almost every song composed and performed by The Beatles. Plus original photographs and full colour illustrations.
(E), NO 17162

The Beatles Complete (Revised)
Re-engraved, revised edition of 'Beatles Complete'. 203 songs – composed and recorded by the group.
Piano/Organ: Piano/vocal, chord symbols (E), NO 18160

The Joy Of Folk Songs
Contains eighty-two popular American songs and songs from other lands, all with lyrics and chord symbols.
(E), YK 21061

Nursery Rhymes And Songs
Over 40 nursery rhymes and songs. Illustrated throughout. Melody lines in standard notation together with chord names. Fun to learn and sing.
(E), AM 60211

It's Easy To Play Children's Songs
Seventeen songs for the modern child – to take their place alongside the traditional nursery rhymes. In easy piano arrangements with lyrics and chord symbols. Includes 'Banks of the Ohio', 'This Ole House' and 'Rivers of Babylon'.
(E), AM 29489

It's Easy To Play Christmas Songs
The world's best-loved carols and Christmas songs – twenty-one of them with words and chord symbols. Includes 'The First Nowell', 'Sleigh Ride' and 'Hark the Herald Angels Sing'.
(E), AM 22641

Hymns And Prayers For Children
Forty-two hymns and prayers. Complete with words, piano accompaniment and chord symbols. Easy to play.
(E), AM 38639

The Joy Of Disney
Easy piano arrangements of songs from Walt Disney's 'Bambi', 'Cinderella' and many others.
(E), WD 10278

Jumping, Laughing And Resting
Over ninety songs for children from 3-10 years old. Melody line in standard notation with chord names. Illustrated.
(E), AM 38621

The Lullaby Book
An illustrated collection of children's lullabies from all over the world. Easy-to-play arrangements with chord names and lyrics.
(A), AM 37029

New Songs For Children
Simplified arrangements of modern tunes such as 'A Windmill in Old Amsterdam', 'Grandad' and 'Yellow Submarine' – thirty in all. Words and chord symbols are included. Delightfully illustrated.
(E), AM 13798
Lyrics only (E), AM 30081

New Songs For Children, The Gingerbread Man Book
Simplified arrangements of the kind of music today's youngsters like to sing and play. 31 songs arranged for piano/vocal with guitar boxes.
(E), AM 36013

The Nursery Rhyme Book
Over one hundred well-loved songs and rhymes. Easy piano arrangement plus words and chord symbols to sixty-four.
(E), AM 26824

Piano Collections & Keyboard Tutors

Classics To Moderns
Each of the six graded volumes in the *Classics to Moderns* Series presents a range of piano music exactly as written by master composers from early Baroque to the present day. The works are ideal for study, sight reading or simply for enjoyment.
Book 1 *(E)*, YK 20014
Book 2 *(E)*, YK 20022
Book 3 *(I)*, YK 20030
Book 4 *(I)*, YK 20048
Book 5 *(I)*, YK 20055
Book 6 *(I)*, YK 20063
Complete Set *(I)*, YK 20071

More Classics To Moderns
Easy, original piano music as written by many famous composers.
Book 1 *(E)*, YK 20121
Book 2 *(E)*, YK 20139
Book 3 *(I)*, YK 20147
Book 4 *(I)*, YK 20154
Book 5 *(I)*, YK 20162
Book 6 *(I)*, YK 20170
Complete Set *(I)*, YK 20188

The Complete Keyboard Player
by Kenneth Baker
Teach yourself to play any make of electronic keyboard, make your keyboard sound like a single instrument or a whole orchestra. Book 1 includes pullout keyboard chart and record.
Book 1 *(E)*, AM 38308
Book 2 *(E)*, AM 38316
Book 3 *(E)*, AM 38324

The Complete Keyboard Player: Songbook 1
Popular numbers to play on the electronic keyboard. Includes 'Brown Girl In The Ring', 'Cecilia', 'Eight Days A Week' and 'Mary's Boy Child'.
(E), AM 39116

The Complete Keyboard Player: Songbook 2
Nineteen popular melodies including 'Amapola', 'Every Breath You Take', 'Here Comes The Sun' and 'Top Of The World'.
(E), AM 39124

The Complete Keyboard Player: Songbook 3
Music for the electronic keyboard, with lyrics to 19 numbers such as 'Georgia On My Mind', 'Eleanor Rigby', 'Those Were The Days' and 'Thank You For The Music'
(E), AM 39132

The Complete Piano Player
by Kenneth Baker
The only piano course based throughout on today's popular songs and famous light classics. Easy to follow text and clear demonstration diagrams. Book 1 with keyboard chart.
Book 1 *(E)*, AM 34828
Book 2 *(E)*, AM 34836
Book 3 *(E)*, AM 34844
Book 4 *(E)*, AM 34851
Book 5 *(E)*, AM 34869

The Complete Piano Player Collection
A unique collection of music. Each book is divided into solos, folk songs, etudes, sonatinas and duets.
Book 1 *(EI)*, PB 40831
Book 2 *(EI)*, PB 40849
Book 3 *(EI)*, PB 40856
Book 4 *(EI)*, PB 40864

Denes Agay's Learning To Play Piano
A progression of melodic pieces and studies teaching the basics step by step. This new course offers a fresh, unhurried, and sound approach to piano study as well as providing a melodic repertoire for the young player.
Book 1: Primer *(A)*, YK20845

Denes Agay's Learning To Play Piano
Book 2: *(A)*, YK20493

Denes Agay's Learning To Play Piano
Book 3 (A), YK20501

Denes Agay's Learning To Play Piano
Book 4 (A), YK20519

Start Playing Creative Keyboard
by Gabriel Butler and Mick Barker
Apply a few simple rules and techniques and discover a new world of creative playing on your keyboard. Useful tips and advice plus 16 famous popular songs.
(D), AM66663

Start Playing Keyboard
by Peter Lavender
An easy-to-follow course which starts you playing electronic keyboard right away, even if you have no knowledge of music. Includes 28 popular songs.
(E), AM 36906

Start Playing Keyboard Book 2
by Peter Lavender
Play 'fingered' chords with the left hand, improve your sight reading and playing technique and progress from SFX letter-note music to standard music notation. 16 popular numbers including 'We've Only Just Begun' and 'Yellow Submarine'.
(D), AM65749

Cats

The fabulous hit musical by Andrew Lloyd Webber. Based on 'Old Possum's Book of Practical Cats' by T.S. Eliot. All the songs arranged for piano with lyrics and chord symbols.
(BCD), AM 31006

Walt Disney Vocal Selections: Cinderella

Arranged for piano, with lyrics and chord symbols.
(B), WD 10039

The Jungle Book

Vocal selection arranged for piano/vocal, with guitar chord symbols.
(ABC), WD 10013

Evita

Musical excerpts and libretto.
(CD), EVM 10005

Fiddler On The Roof

Vocal selections from the show. 11 numbers including 'If I Were A Rich Man' and 'Sunrise, Sunset'.
(D), AM 39520

Jesus Christ Superstar

Musical excerpts and complete libretto.
(CD), LE 11110

The New Illustrated Disney Songbook

Seventy-three memorable Disney songs from such favourite films as 'Snow White and the Seven Dwarfs', 'Pinocchio', 'Cinderella', 'The Jungle Book' and many more. Arranged for piano/vocal with guitar boxes. Full colour illustrations.
(CD), OP44031

Walt Disney's Bambi Songbook

All the songs from the film. Arranged for piano/vocal with chord boxes. Colour illustrations.
(AB), CC11321

Smike

Libretto *(B), AV 51860*
Vocal Score *(B), AV 51878*

The Walt Disney Songbook

Walt Disney favourites from 'Davy Crockett', 'The Jungle Book', 'Bedknobs And Broomsticks', 'Cinderella', 'Mary Poppins', 'The Happiest Millionaire', 'Pinocchio', 'Snow White' and other shows. 25 numbers for piano with lyrics and chord symbols.
(C), AM19316

The Complete Guitar Player Music Writing Book

The only music writing book specially compiled for guitarists. Enables you to keep a complete record of your own songs and repertoire.
64pp, AM 34208

The Complete Guitar Player Music Writing Pad

Sixty-four pages, each containing ten blank chord diagrams and 6 staves for notation.
64pp, AM 34216

Woodstock Music Manuscript Paper

A4, 12 stave, *32pp, WO 10166*
A4, 12 stave, spiral, *32pp, WO 10174*
A5L, 6 stave, spiral *32pp, WO 10224*
A5L, 6 stave stitched, *32pp, WO 10216*
A4, 12 stave, punched, *48pp, WO 10182*
A4, 12 stave, *64pp, WO 10190*
A4, 12 stave, spiral, *64pp, WO 10208*

The Complete Guitar Player Video

with Russ Shipton
Full colour teaching video lasting 60 minutes which is an important addition to The Complete Guitar Player series. A self-contained home study course.
VHS *(CD), OV 10002*
Beta *(CD), OV 10010*

How To Read Music

with Frederick Noad
Even if you have never read a note of music, this 51-minute, full-colour video will teach you how. Ideal for classroom or private teaching.
VHS *(CD), OV 10028*
Beta *(CD), OV 10093*

Jigsaw

Popular tunes for school orchestras. This series of flexible arrangements may be used with players of wide ranging abilities. Pack includes Conductor Score and parts for instruments including piano, recorder, violin, euphonium, cello, flute, bass, oboe and trumpet etc.
EastEnders (BC), AM65798
I Know Him So Well (BC), AM66747

We Wish You A Merry Christmas

by Barrie Carson Turner
Five variations scored for classroom ensemble and piano. This pack includes: piano/conductor score, 6 recorder and 4 each tuned and untuned percussion parts.
(BC), AM65202

Clarinet

Flute

Penny Whistle

Clarinet

Beatles, Themes And Variations: Clarinet
Seven Beatles themes with three variations. Pull-out piano accompaniment. Also for flute and trumpet.
(I), NO 17873

Graded Solos For Clarinet
Forty popular songs selected and arranged by Robin de Smet. Also for flute and trumpet.
(EI), AM 33598

Lennon & McCartney For Clarinet
This book presents over fifty compositions arranged for the clarinet. Also for trumpet and flute.
(I), NO 17725

100 Solos: Clarinet
Graded solos for players of all standards. Each piece is complete in itself and requires no piano accompaniment. Also for flute, saxophone, trumpet and violin.
(EI), AM 33689

101 Popular Songs For Trumpet And Clarinet
Arranged in solo and duet form. A collection of popular and traditional tunes.
(EI), HS 10445

The Complete Clarinet Player
by Paul Harvey
Based on popular songs and light classics. Clear text, diagrams, photographs.
Book 1
Blow your first notes and learn the rudiments of music. Play songs such as 'Love Me Tender', 'Yellow Submarine' . . . Fingering chart.
(CD), AM62613
Book 2 (CD), AM62621
Book 3 (CD), AM62639
Book 4 (CD), AM62647

Associated Board Examination Grades
(E) Elementary – Grades 1-3
(I) Intermediate – Grades 4-6
(Ad) Advanced – Grades 6-8
(T) Teacher's Book

Flute

Beatles, Themes And Variations: Flute
Seven Beatles themes with three variations. Pull-out piano accompaniment. Also for clarinet and trumpet.
(I), NO 17865

50 Selected Children's Classics
Includes 'Arabesque', 'Barcarolle' and 'Canon in D'. Also for recorder and piano.
(E), HS 10551

Flute Solos (EFS 38)
Effective arrangements of over 50 pieces. The wide range of compositions includes works of Beethoven, Brahms, Dvořák, Schubert and many others as well as folk songs, dances' jigs and reels from all over the world. Each piece includes piano accompaniment.
(BCD), AM 40197

Graded Solos For Flute
Forty popular songs selected and arranged by Robin de Smet. Also for clarinet and trumpet.
(BD), AM 33812

Lennon & McCartney For Flute
This book presents over fifty compositions arranged for the flute. Also for trumpet and clarinet.
(I), NO 17717

100 Solos: Flute
Graded solos for players of all standards. Each piece is complete and does not require piano accompaniment. Also for clarinet, saxophone, trumpet and violin.
(EI), AM 33812

One Hundred And One Solos For The Flute
An outstanding collection of popular and light classical music arranged by Robin De Smet. Includes 'Chanson Triste', 'EastEnders' and 'The Power Of Love'.
(CD), AM63538

Selected Flute Solos (EFS 101)
This volume contains a group of the finest standard flute solos selected for their diversity in style and suitability for concert and contest use. Among the selections are works by Pessard, Chaminade, Mozart, Handel, Mendelssohn, Gluck, Fauré and Godard. All have piano accompaniment.
(Ad), AM 40403

The Complete Flute Player
by John Sands
The only flute course using popular tunes. Clear text, photographs and diagrams.
Book 1
Assembling the flute and producing your first sounds. Left hand notes, music notation and 7 keys. Music by Lennon & McCartney and John Denver etc.
(CD), AM62852
Book 2 (CD), AM62860
Book 3 (CD), AM62878
Book 4 (CD), AM62886

Penny Whistle

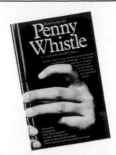

How To Play The Penny Whistle
by Gina Landor & Phil Cleaver
No previous knowledge required. Illustrated with clear diagrams. Also contains many popular tunes to play.
(E), AM 27137

The Penny Whistle Book
by Robin Williamson
A complete guide to the penny whistle for beginning to advanced players using a new systematic approach to fingering. Contains information on modal playing and 56 penny whistle tunes. Superb as a beginner's text, also of great use to the advanced player.
(EIAd), OK 63271

Abba Songs For The Recorder
A selection of favourite Abba songs specially arranged for the recorder. Published complete with lyrics and guitar diagrams plus a two-page introduction to playing the recorder. Includes 'Waterloo' and 'Knowing Me, Knowing You'.
(I), AM 19720

Appalachian Folk Songs For Recorder
by Ralph Wm. Zeitlin
Thirty traditional folk songs and tunes arranged as solos and duets for soprano and alto recorders.
(I), AM 35650

Around The World With My Recorder
by Harry Dexter
Includes 101 selected song favourites in easy to play recorder arrangements.
(E), HS 11542

Bach For Recorder
by Cliff Tobey
Solos and duets arranged for soprano and tenor recorders.
(IAd), AY 15406

Baroque & Folk Tunes For The Recorder
An unusual collection of music arranged for the recorder – fifty pieces from over 300 years of music.
(I), AM 17948

Beatles For Recorder
Easy new arrangements by Robin de Smet, of famous Beatles songs. Thirty tunes with chord symbols.
(E), AM 18434

Beatles Songs For The Recorder
Outstanding collection of Beatles songs arranged specially for recorder. Complete with lyrics and guitar diagrams. Includes a two-page introduction to playing the recorder.
(I), NO 17394

Children's Songs For The Recorder
Twenty-five songs especially arranged for recorder with lyrics and guitar chord boxes.
(I), AM 13673

Christmas Songs For The Recorder
Over 20 of the best known Christmas carols arranged for recorder with lyrics and guitar boxes.
(E), AM 20157

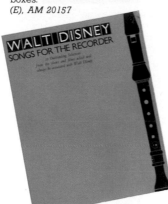

Walt Disney Songs For The Recorder
Twenty-five outstanding selections from the shows and films which will always be associated with Walt Disney. Includes lyrics and guitar boxes.
(I), WD 10070

Early Music For Recorder
arranged by Robin de Smet
Easy new arrangements of airs and dances from the 10th to the 16th century. 47 tunes with chord symbols.
(E), AM 36542

Elizabethan Music For Recorder
by Ralph Wm. Zeitlin
Solos, duets, trios and rounds arranged for soprano, alto and tenor recorders.
(I), AY 15315

50 Selected Children's Classics
Includes 'Arabesque', 'Barcarolle', 'Canon in D'. Also for flute and piano.
(E), HS 10569

50 Songs For Recorder Book 1
For recorder with guitar accompaniment. Includes 'California Dreaming', 'Fernando' and 'Bright Eyes'.
(I), AM 29885

50 Songs For Recorder Book 2
For recorder and guitar accompaniment. Includes 'Top of the World', 'Little Buttercup' and 'Sailing'.
(I), AM 29893

Film Music For The Recorder
Twenty-eight well known film titles arranged for recorder, with lyrics and guitar boxes.
(I), AM 25701

Film And TV Themes For The Recorder
Over 20 notable tunes used as film and TV themes with lyrics and guitar chord boxes.
(I), AM 13962

Folk Songs For The Recorder
Twenty-seven famous folk songs arranged for recorder, with lyrics and guitar boxes.
(I), AM 29000

How To Play The Recorder
Pocket size recorder tutor which is a complete course for the beginner that is easy and fun to play.
(E), AM 35551

Hymns For Recorder
Easy new arrangements by Robin de Smet of 34 best loved hymn tunes. With chord symbols and words.
(E), AM 36559

Irish Music For Recorder
New easy arrangements by Robin de Smet of famous Irish songs and melodies. 30 tunes with chord symbols.
(E), AM 36534

Jazz For The Recorder
A contrasting selection of popular and jazz standards. Includes lyrics and guitar chord boxes.
(I), AM 28994

Paul McCartney: Songs for the Recorder
Twenty-seven songs including 'Mull of Kintyre', 'My Love'. With lyrics and guitar diagrams plus a 2 page introduction to playing the recorder.
(I), MY 70358

My Very First Recorder Songbook. Book A
Fifteen easy to play songs, folk tunes and songs from shows and films. With piano accompaniment and separate recorder part.
(E), AM 34158
Book B
(E), AM 34166

New Popular Songs For The Recorder
Published complete with lyrics and guitar chord boxes.
(E), AM 31501

Oliver: Songs For The Recorder
Outstanding selection from the show, with lyrics and guitar chord boxes, plus a six-page introduction to playing the recorder.
(I), AM 13368

Paul Simon Songs For The Recorder
Twenty songs including lyrics and guitar diagrams plus a two-page introduction to playing the recorder.
(I), PS 10016

Songs And Dances Of England
An outstanding collection of songs and dances from England's musical heritage. Arranged for voice and recorder, penny whistle or flute, or other suitable 'C' instruments.
(EI), AM 31428

Songs And Dances Of Ireland
A collection of songs from Ireland's rich musical heritage. All arranged for voice and recorder, penny whistle or flute, or other suitable 'C' instrument.
(EI), AM 31402

Songs And Dances Of Scotland
An exciting collection of songs and dances all arranged for voice and recorder, flute, penny whistle or other 'C' instrument. With chord symbols and guitar diagrams, plus full lyrics.
(EI), AM 31410

Cat Stevens Songs For The Recorder
Complete with lyrics and guitar boxes. Plus a two page introduction to playing the recorder.
(I), AM 23425

10 Famous Pop Songs For Recorder
For solos or ensemble playing. Piano accompaniment available. Can be played with any other instrument in the series. Includes 'Michelle' and 'Unforgettable'. Lyrics and chord symbols. Also for violin, saxophone, flute, clarinet and trumpet.
(E), AM 28614

Piano Accompaniments
(E), AM 28507

Together For Two Recorders And Guitar
A variety of music ranging from Purcell to Pop. Mozart's 'Allegro' is joined by melodies such as 'Clementine' and 'Rivers Of Babylon'. With lyrics, chord symbols and guitar boxes.
Book 1 *(E), AM 29901*

Together For Two Recorders And Guitar
For C Recorders and guitars playing in ensemble. Boccherini's 'Minuet' to 'Yesterday'. Lyrics, chord symbols, and guitar boxes.
Book 2 *(E), AM 29919*

Associated Board Examination Grades
(E) Elementary – Grades 1-3
(I) Intermediate – Grades 4-6
(Ad) Advanced – Grades 6-8
(T) Teacher's Book

Continued . . .

Saxophone

101 Easy Sax Solos & Duets
A collection of popular and traditional tunes.
(E), HS 11864

100 Solos: Saxophone
Graded solos for players of all standards. Each piece is complete in itself and requires no piano accompaniment. Also for clarinet, flute, recorder, trumpet and violin.
(EI), AM 33697

The Complete Saxophone Player
by Raphael Ravenscroft
This course is based on popular tunes and light classics. With clear text, diagrams and photographs it will prove easy to understand even to those with no knowledge of music.
Book 1 (CD), AM62712
Book 2 (CD), AM62720
Book 3 (CD), AM62738
Book 4 (CD), AM62746

Trumpet

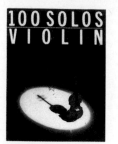

The Complete Trumpet Player
by Don Bateman
Based on popular songs and light classics. Clear text, diagrams, photographs.
Book 1
Rudiments of music, technique, the notes Low G to High D. Play songs such as 'I'd Like To Teach The World To Sing' and 'Edelweiss'.
(CD), AM39207
Book 2 (CD), AM39215
Book 3 (CD), AM39223
Book 4 (CD), AM39231

101 Solos For The Trumpet
arranged by Robin De Smet
An outstanding collection of music for trumpet covering a wide range of popular and light classical music.
(CD), AM61870

Popular Solos For The Trumpet
Over 30 hits from today's top artists. Includes 'Caribbean Queen', 'Walk Of Life', 'We Don't Need Another Hero' and 'When The Going Gets Tough'. No piano accompaniment required.
(CD), AM63108

Violin

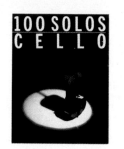

100 Solos For Violin
Graded solos for players of all standards. The pieces are complete in themselves and require no piano accompaniment. Includes 'Dancing Queen', 'Michelle' and 'English Country Garden'.
(CD), AM33671

100 Cello Solos
Graded solos for players of all standards. The pieces are complete in themselves and require no accompaniment.
(CD), AM63231

Cello Solos
Easy to intermediate arrangements designed to bring out the finest qualities of the cello.
(CD), AM64486

Christmas Solos

Christmas Solos For The Clarinet
arranged by Robin De Smet
A unique collection of 49 traditional and up-to-date Christmas songs including 'Santa Claus Is Comin' To Town', 'When Santa Got Stuck Up The Chimney', 'Winter Wonderland' and many more. With chord symbols.
(CD), AM65020

Christmas Solos For The Flute
arranged by Robin De Smet
A unique collection of 53 traditional and up-to-date Christmas songs including 'Frosty The Snowman', 'I Believe In Father Christmas', 'Santa Claus Is Comin' To Town'. With chord symbols.
(CD), AM65038

Christmas Solos For The Recorder
arranged by Robin De Smet
A unique collection of 50 traditional and up-to-date Christmas songs including 'Away In A Manger', 'Silent Night', 'Santa Claus Is Comin' To Town' and 'Winter Wonderland'.
(CD), AM65046

Christmas Solos For The Bb Saxophone
arranged by Robin De Smet
A unique collection of more than 50 traditional and up-to-date Christmas songs including 'The First Nowell', 'Santa Claus Is Comin' To Town', 'Silent Night' and 'Winter Wonderland'. With chord symbols.
(CD), AM65061

Christmas Solos For The Trumpet
arranged by Robin De Smet
A unique collection of 49 traditional and up-to-date Christmas songs including 'Santa Claus Is Comin' To Town', 'When Santa Got Stuck Up The Chimney', 'Winter Wonderland' and many more. With chord symbols.
(CD), AM65053

Christmas Solos For The Violin
Standard carols and songs for the festive season arranged for the beginning-to-intermediate player. Chord symbols facilitate optional piano or guitar accompaniment.
(CD), AM67133

All books in this catalogue are available from your local music dealer. In case of difficulty contact:
Music Sales Limited
Newmarket Road, Bury St Edmunds IP33 3YB.

Tongueing

The material on this page may be assigned whenever the teacher feels the need for this style of playing development.

Staccato

Staccato, meaning detached, separated, is a style of tongueing used in clarinet playing to denote a short crisp note. Notes to be played staccato are marked with a dot, placed over or under them.

* For explanation of semiquavers see Lesson 33.

**For explanation of triplets see Lesson 37.

LESSON 19

OBJECTIVES:
1. Correlation of notes in the upper register, (name and position on staff) with proper fingerings.
2. To learn the use of the register key.
3. Learning to use these new notes in the playing of melodies and a duet (practise both parts)

Five Notes in the Clarion or Upper Register

Up to this time you have been playing in the low or chalumeau register, from low E to 3rd line B♭. Starting with this lesson we introduce the clarion or upper register which extends from 3rd line B♮ to high C, two lines above the staff. Unlike the flute, oboe or saxophone, which overblow in the octave (8 notes higher), the clarinet, by opening the register key (R), overblows 12 notes (an octave and a fifth) higher. To apply this principle, play middle C (preparatory study (a)), then add register key (R) with the left thumb, (thumb hole must be kept closed at the same time) then by slightly stretching the lower lip, sound G. (first space above the staff) Apply this same rule to the other notes in this exercise. BE SURE TO LEARN THESE NEW FINGERINGS.

Preparatory Study

Home work   Write line of notes used in this lesson. Divide into bars and mark as before.

OBJECTIVES: 1. To learn the use of four additional notes in the upper register.
        2. The use of slurred notes in the playing of an Etude.
      (exercise in breath control)

Four Additional Notes in the Clarion (upper) Register

Apply the same principle as in the preceding lesson.

Preparatory Study

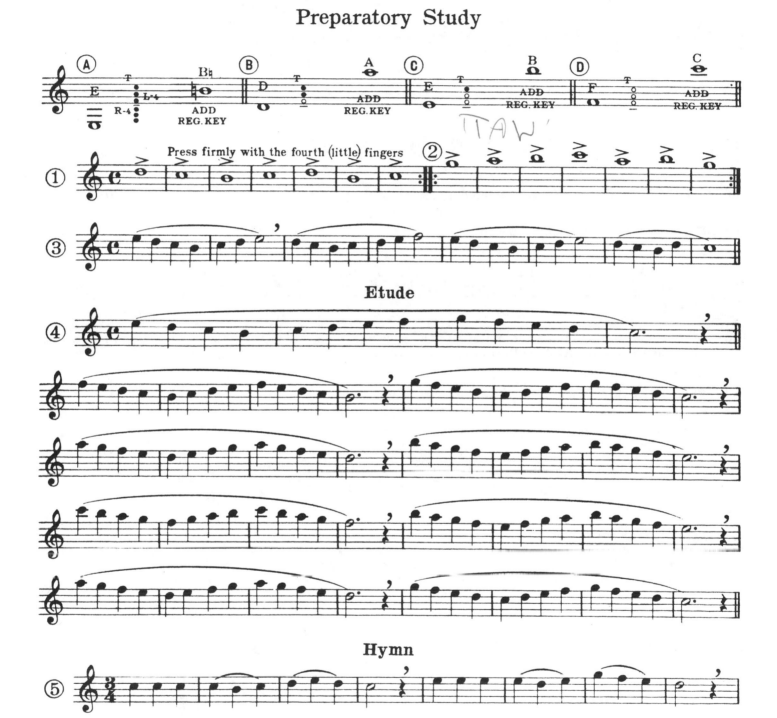

Etude

Hymn

TEST QUESTIONS ON LESSONS 16-20

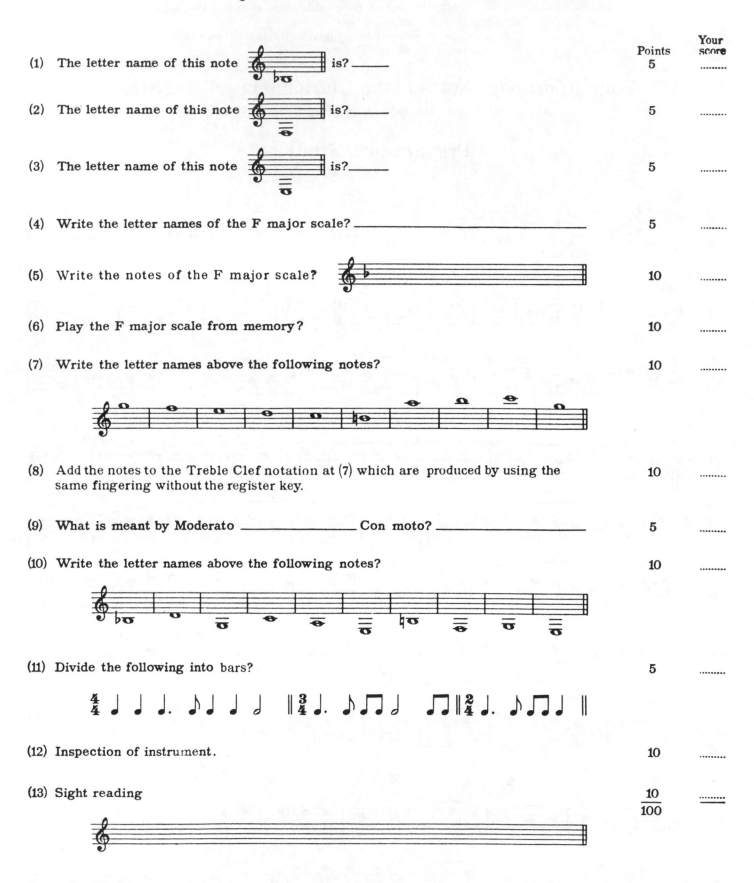

	Points	Your score
(1) The letter name of this note ___ is? ___	5	....
(2) The letter name of this note ___ is? ___	5	....
(3) The letter name of this note ___ is? ___	5	....
(4) Write the letter names of the F major scale? ___	5	....
(5) Write the notes of the F major scale?	10	....
(6) Play the F major scale from memory?	10	....
(7) Write the letter names above the following notes?	10	....
(8) Add the notes to the Treble Clef notation at (7) which are produced by using the same fingering without the register key.	10	....
(9) What is meant by Moderato ___ Con moto? ___	5	....
(10) Write the letter names above the following notes?	10	....
(11) Divide the following into bars?	5	....
(12) Inspection of instrument.	10	....
(13) Sight reading	10	....
	100	

TEACHER: Write line of notes in the clarion register.

LESSON 21

OBJECTIVES:
1. To learn the principle of the upper register as compared to the lower in regard to fingering.
2. To apply this principle in the playing of familiar melodies.
3. Slurring from one register to another, both up and down.

Comparison Between the Upper and Lower Registers

Short familiar melodies using the same fingering for lower and upper registers.

Christmas Song

Folk Song

Slurring from Lower to Upper Register (Same fingering)
(Use firm fingering)

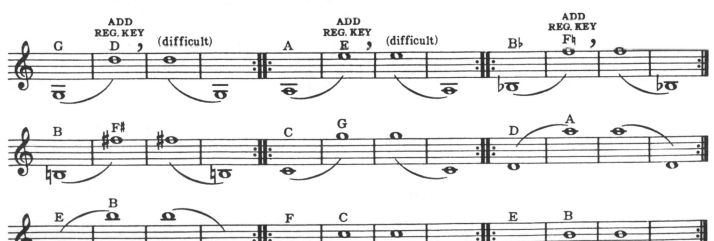

LESSON 22

OBJECTIVES: 1. Playing melodies in the octave using different
fingerings.
2. To learn to slur octaves.

Octave (eight) means an interval of eight scale degrees higher or lower from any given note. Ex.(C to C)
(D to D) etc.

Playing the Same Melodies in the Octave
Using lower and upper registers

God Save The Queen

Carey

Crusader's Hymn

Slurring Octaves

OBJECTIVE: To learn the principle of fingering in crossing from
one register to another.

LESSON 24

OBJECTIVE: Application of the principle of crossing registers
in the playing of familiar melodies.

Changing Register Through "A"

Reuben and Rachel

How Can I Leave Thee

Folk-Song

Auld Lang Syne

Old Scotch Air

Massa's in the Cold, Cold Ground

Foster

OBJECTIVES: 1.   To learn to change registers through B♭.
                    2.   To learn the F Major scale and arpeggio. (upper octave)
                    3.   The playing of familiar melodies in the key of F Major.

Changing Register Through "B♭"

Scale of F Major (*upper octave)

Arpeggio (broken chord)

All Through the Night

Hymn

Blue Bells of Scotland

*Review lower octave in lesson 17.

TEST QUESTIONS ON LESSONS 21-25

	Points	Your score
(1) The interval between these notes ... is called? _____	5	....
(2) Write the upper octave of the F major scale?	9	....
(3) Play the F major scale in two octaves.	5	....
(4) Write the following melody an octave higher.	8	....
(5) Add correct time signature to the following bars?	6	....
(6) Place a sharp (♯) before the notes affected by the key signature in the following line?	8	....
(7) Name the key of the following signatures?	9	....
(8) Mark the count under the following?	5	....
(9) Write the correct note after the following that you would play with the same fingering plus the register key?	10	....
(10) What is the meaning of Allegro? _____ Andante? _____	5	....
(11) Inspection of instrument.	10	....
(12) Sight reading.	10	....
	10	....
	100	

TEACHER: Write two lines of notes, one in the **upper** register, and one in the lower register as a check on fingering.

LESSON 26

OBJECTIVES: 1. To change registers through B♮.
2. To learn the G Major scale and arpeggio.
3. To play familiar melodies in the key of G Major.
4. To learn the meaning of dynamics. (volume of tone)

Changing Register Through "B♮"

Scale of G Major (upper octave)

Arpeggio

G Major Scale and Arpeggio in Two Octaves

O Come, All Ye Faithful

Home, Sweet Home

*Hold little fingers down throughout bracketed passages.

Supplementary Material for Lessons 24, 25 and 26

Long, Long Ago

D.S.—Dal Segno (go back to this sign 𝄋) and play to *Fine* (End)

LESSON 27

OBJECTIVES: 1. Understanding and playing chromatics.
2. Knowledge of enharmonic notes.
3. Learning new fingerings.

Chromatics

The word "chromatic" means moving by semitones. A chromatic scale is one that ascends or descends by half steps.

ENHARMONIC notes sound the same though given a different name because they are on different degrees of the staff. Ex. F♯-G♭.

(L) means left hand, (R) means right hand.

BE SURE TO LEARN THE PROPER FINGERING FOR BOTH ASCENDING AND DESCENDING CHROMATIC SCALES.

Chromatic Scale of C in Two Octaves

* See next page for alternative fingering of these notes.

Important New Fingering for the Following Enharmonic Notes

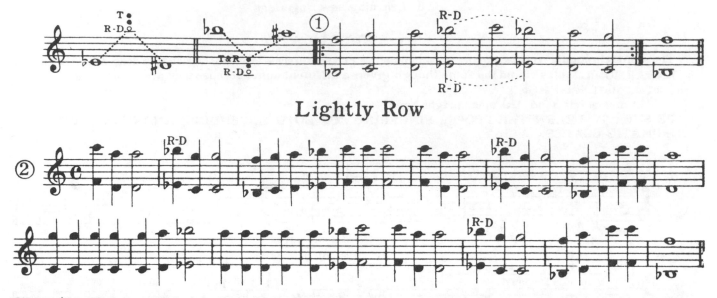

Lightly Row

Supplementary Material for Chromatics and "Bridging" the Registers

Diligent practice of the exercises on this page will give you command of all chromatic intervals in practical use. Practise exercises **3 to 7** as indicated, also play slurring four and eight notes. Play slowly at first gradually increasing the speed.

Chromatic Etude

Wohlfahrt

The use of Accidentals and Chromatics
in the Playing of Familiar Melodies

LEARN TO TAKE PARTICULAR NOTICE OF THE KEY SIGNATURE BEFORE PLAYING

The Star Spangled Banner

John Stafford Smith

REVIEW D MAJOR SCALE, PAGE 45

America, the Beautiful

Ward

Scales and Arpeggios (Chords)

The material on this page may be assigned whenever the teacher feels the need for scale and chord studies.
Play the following scales and chords as indicated; also play as follows:

ALWAYS NOTICE THE KEY SIGNATURE; IT IS A GUIDE FOR PROPER FINGERING.

(L) means left hand. (R) means right hand.

Place one or both fourth fingers on B and C keys according to the notes to follow.

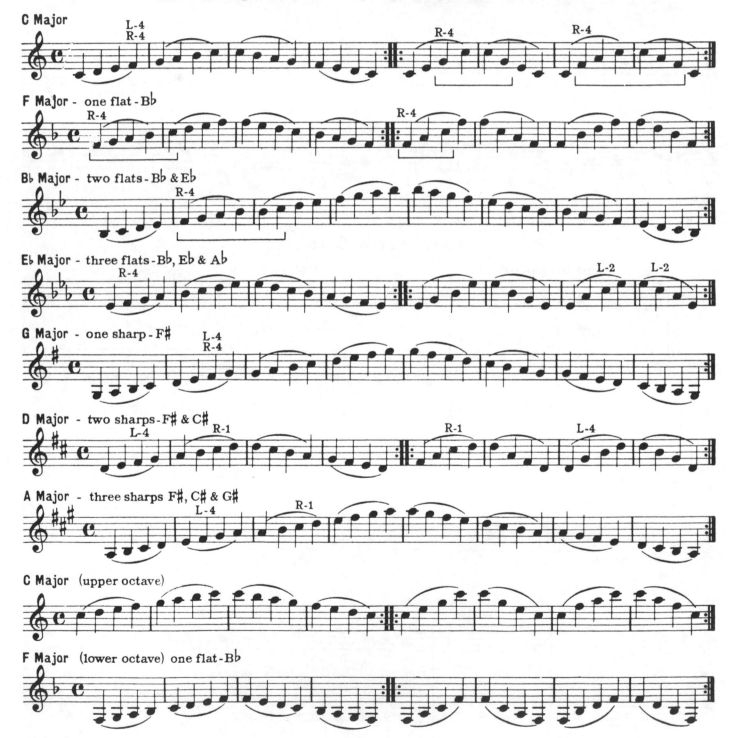

Home work: Place a sharp or flat before the notes affected by the key signatures in the above scales.

Important Assignment*

Complete the examples of the scale study, (Ex. 1) using the various keys as indicated. Place a sharp or flat in front of the notes affected by the key signature. Play what you write.

Scale Study

Key of _____ flats are _____

Key of _____ sharps are _____

Key of _____ flats are _____

Key of _____ flat is _____

Key of _____ sharp is _____

*Teacher: These exercises should be assigned with the study of the corresponding scales in the preceding lesson.

Supplementary Material in the keys of B♭, E♭ & A Major*

Jeanie With the Light Brown Hair

Foster

Old Folks at Home
(Duet)

Foster

Cradle Song

Brahms

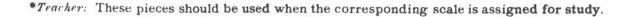

*Teacher: These pieces should be used when the corresponding scale is assigned for study.

LESSON 28

OBJECTIVES: 1. Learning a new rhythm.
2. Understanding Alla breve. (cut time) ($\frac{2}{2}$ time)
3. Application of acquired knowledge in playing accidentals.

Alla breve or $\frac{2}{2}$ time

Alla breve, ($\frac{2}{2}$) or cut time ¢ is played the same as $\frac{2}{4}$ time. Each note having half the value as in $\frac{4}{4}$ time, a minim being the unit of a beat.

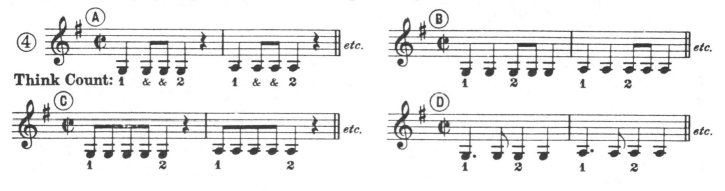

Rhythm Drills

Play the following rhythm patterns, (A)-(B) etc. using the G Major scale (one or two octaves) as an exercise.

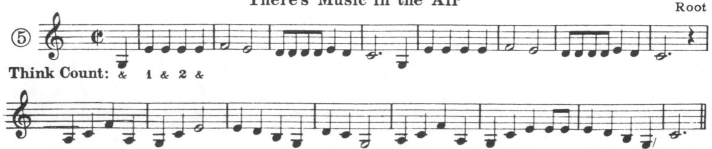

There's Music in the Air

Root

LESSON 29

OBJECTIVES: 1. Continuation of Alla breve (cut time).
2. The playing of a full length march.
3. Application of acquired knowledge

Advancement March*

* All marches generally consist of an introduction, 1st and 2nd strain, each repeated, followed by a Trio. The key of the trio is always a fifth lower than that of the first part.

** This sign ⅌ means to repeat the preceding bar.

Supplementary Material using Alla Breve (Cut time)

NOTICE KEY SIGNATURES AND WHAT THEY MEAN

A Capital Ship

Old English Tune

Theme from Der Freischütz

von Weber

College Song**

* *a tempo*, - in the original tempo.

** This theme (melody) was used by Brahms in his Academic Festival Overture.

LESSON 30

OBJECTIVES: 1. To learn another new rhythm.
2. Knowledge and use of the rhythm of $\frac{6}{8}$ time.
3. Counting six to a bar and two to a bar.
4. Application of new rhythm in familiar melodies.

Six-Eight Time

Count six beats to each bar in slow tempo - a quaver (♪) being the unit of a beat.
Count two beats to each bar in fast tempo - a dotted crotchet (♩.) being the unit of a beat.
Use the rhythm patterns below in playing other scales you know to gain facility in fingering.

Home work: Write line of notes, using different rhythm patterns in $\frac{6}{8}$ time.

LESSON 31

OBJECTIVES: 1. Continuation of six-eight time. (slow)
2. Counting six beats to a bar.
3. To learn the meaning of ritard. (rit.)
4. Use of dynamics. cresc. dim.

It Came Upon a Midnight Clear

Drink to Me Only With Thine Eyes
(Duet)

Old English Air

Rit., Abbreviation for ritenuto - gradually slower in speed.

LESSON 32

OBJECTIVES:
1. Continuation of six-eight time. (fast)
2. Counting two beats to a bar. (march time)
3. Application of acquired knowledge in the playing of a duet.
4. Playing of a march in six-eight time.

The Lion Hunt
(Duet)

Saverio

Progress March

Tempo di Marcia

C. F. H.

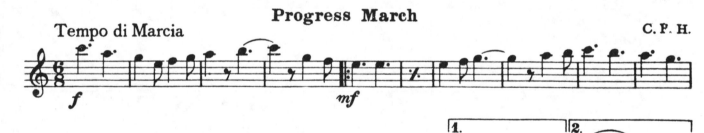

Trio Key of ___ flat is ___

TEST QUESTIONS ON LESSONS 26-32

	Points	Your score

(1) Write the upper octave of the G major scale? — 10 ....

(2) What is the meaning of (*f*) _____ (*p*) _____ (*mf*) _____ ? — 5 ....

(3) What are enharmonic notes? _____ — 5 ....

(4) Write the enharmonic equivalents of the following notes? — 5 ....

(5) What is meant by chromatic? _____ — 5 ....

(6) This sign ¢ means? _____ — 5 ....

(7) A minim in (¢) time receives _____ count? — 5 ....

(8) What is meant by six-eight ($\frac{6}{8}$) time? _____ — 5 ....

(9) This note _____ in slow $\frac{6}{8}$ time has _____ counts? — 5 ....

(10) The above note in fast $\frac{6}{8}$ time has _____ counts? — 5 ....

(11) This note _____ in slow $\frac{6}{8}$ time has _____ counts? In fast time? _____ — 5 ....

(12) Mark the count under the following? Slow tempo. — 5 ....

(13) Divide the following into bars? (Note time signature.) — 5 ....

(14) This sign ⅍ means? _____ — 5 ....

(15) In $\frac{6}{8}$ march time (fast) the count is _____ beats to each bar? — 5 ....

(16) Inspection of instrument. — 10 ....

(17) Sight reading. — 10 ....

100

TEACHER: Write line of notes in slow six-eight time in the key of F.

LESSON 33

OBJECTIVES: 1. To learn the meaning and use of semiquavers.
    (a) Equivalents.
    (b) Counting semiquavers.
2. The playing of etudes and pieces using semiquavers.

Semiquavers

A semiquaver is equal to half the value of a quaver Two semiquavers equal one quaver and four semiquavers equal one crotchet Abbreviations for semiquavers

Bird Song

Kingdom Comin'

Mendelssohn

Scale Study*

*Practise the above scale study with staccato tongueing.

**In this piece, which requires a slow movement, (andante) it is better to divide the $\frac{2}{4}$ time into $\frac{4}{8}$ (one count to each quaver)

OBJECTIVES: 1. To learn dotted quavers and semiquavers, legato..
2. To learn the correct division of each beat.
3. Application of new rhythm.

Dotted Quavers and Semiquavers
Legato (Connected)

This is one of the more difficult rhythms to learn. The dotted quaver is equal to three semiquavers. Always feel a division of four on each beat when playing this rhythm, three on the dotted quaver and one on the semiquaver.

BE SURE TO PLAY THE DOTTED QUAVER LONG ENOUGH AND THE SEMIQUAVER SHORT ENOUGH.

Largo
(New World Symphony)
Duet

Dvořàk

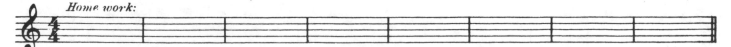

Home work: Write line of notes, using dotted quavers and semiquavers.
cresc. – Gradually louder.

LESSON 35

OBJECTIVES: 1. To learn dotted quavers and semiquavers, **staccato**.
2. Application of this difficult rhythm in familiar melodies using $\frac{2}{4}$ and $\frac{4}{4}$ time.

Dotted Quavers and Semiquavers
Staccato (**Detached**)

Dotted quavers and semiquavers, played staccato (detached) are separated by a short pause. Take notice how these notes are written and how they are actually played.

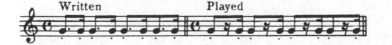

Joy to the World
(Duet)

Handel

Battle Hymn of the Republic

Steffe

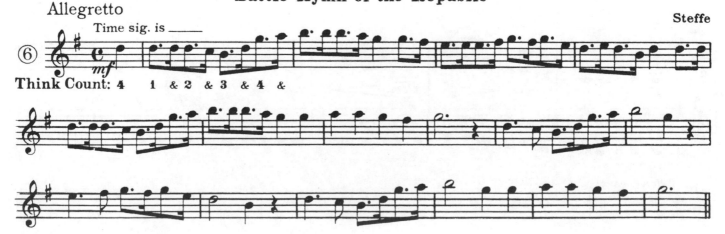

Home work: Memorize one of the melodies on this page.

LESSON 36

OBJECTIVE: Continued application of dotted quavers and semiquavers in $\frac{3}{4}$ and $\frac{6}{8}$ time.

Maryland, My Maryland
(Duet)

Silent Night, Holy Night
(Duet)

Grüber

Triplets

Triplets are groups of three notes played in the time of two notes of the same value. They are indicated by a figure 3 and a slur placed over or under a group of three notes. A triplet of quavers is equal to two quavers or one crotchet.

A bar of 2/4 containing two triplets is the same as a bar of 6/8 in march time.

① Allegro
This   Equals   This

②
Key of —

③

④

God Save The Queen
(Variation in Triplets)

Carey

⑤

rit.

Scale Study

Supplementary Material

Santa Lucia

Tramp, Tramp, Tramp

Root

Think Count. 4   1   2   3   4

Dixie

Dan Emmett

* **Andantino - Slower than Andante**

** In $\frac{3}{8}$ time a quaver is the unit of a beat. (♪) equals 1 beat, (♩) equals 2 beats, and a (♩.) equals 3 beats.

TEST QUESTIONS ON LESSONS 33-37

		Points	Your score

(1) These   are _____ ?   5   ....

(2) Four (4) of the above notes equal a _____ ?   5   ....

(3) Divide the following into bars?   5   ....

(4) Circle the notes in the following line that begin each beat?   8   ....

(5) A 𝅗𝅥 is equal to _____ semiquavers?   5   ....

(6) A ♪. is equal to _____ semiquavers?   5   ....

(7) This is equal to a _____ ?   5   ....

(8) Write five bars in 4/4 time, using dotted-quavers and semiquavers?   10   ....

(9) Divide the following into bars?   7   ....

(10) Write a line of notes in 3/4 time using dotted-quavers and semiquavers.   10   ....

(11) Write a line of notes in 6/8 time using dotted-quavers and semiquavers?   10   ....

(12) These are called? _____   5   ....

(13) Inspection of instrument.   10   ....

(14) Sight reading.   10   ....

             100

TEACHER: Write line of notes using dotted-quavers and semiquavers using slurs, accidentals etc.

FINAL GRADE ON COMPLETION

Two Quartets for four Clarinets

Old Folks At Home

Foster

Old Black Joe

Foster

Printed in England by Commercial Colour Press, London E7.